the book of
Psalms 1-50

ONE CHAPTER A DAY

GoodMorningGirls.org

Psalms 1-50

Welcome! We are so glad you are joining us.

God created us to walk with Him, to know Him, and to be loved by Him. He is our living well, and when we drink from the water He continually provides, His living water will change the entire course of our lives.

Jesus said: "Whoever drinks of the water that I will give him will never be thirsty again. The water that I will give him will become in him a spring of water welling up to eternal life." ~ John 4:14 (ESV)

So let's begin.

The method we use here at GMG is called the **SOAK** method.

- ❐ **S**—The S stands for *Scripture*—Read the chapter for the day. Then choose 1-2 verses and write them out word for word. (There is no right or wrong choice—just let the Holy Spirit guide you.)

- ❐ **O**—The O stands for *Observation*—Look at the verse or verses you wrote out. Write 1 or 2 observations. What stands out to you? What do you learn about the character of God from these verses? Is there a promise, command or teaching?

- ❐ **A**—The A stands for *Application*—Personalize the verses. What is God saying to you? How can you apply them to your life? Are there any changes you need to make or an action to take?

- ❐ **K**—The K stands for *Kneeling in Prayer*—Pause, kneel and pray. Confess any sin God has revealed to you today. Praise God for His word. Pray the passage over your own life or someone you love. Ask God to help you live out your applications.

SOAK God's word into your heart and squeeze every bit of nourishment you can out of each day's scripture reading. Soon you will find your life transformed by the renewing of your mind!

Walk with the King!

Courtney

WomenLivingWell.org, GoodMorningGuys.org

GMG Bible Coloring Chart

COLORS	KEYWORDS
PURPLE	God, Jesus, Holy Spirit, Saviour, Messiah
PINK	women of the Bible, family, marriage, parenting, friendship, relationships
RED	love, kindness, mercy, compassion, peace, grace
GREEN	faith, obedience, growth, fruit, salvation, fellowship, repentance
YELLOW	worship, prayer, praise, doctrine, angels, miracles, power of God, blessings
BLUE	wisdom, teaching, instruction, commands
ORANGE	prophecy, history, times, places, kings, genealogies, people, numbers, covenants, vows, visions, oaths, future
BROWN/GRAY	Satan, sin, death, hell, evil, idols, false teachers, hypocrisy, temptation

Introduction to the Book of Psalms

Down through the centuries, believers have turned to the book of Psalms, as their favorite book of the Bible. Do you need encouragement, comfort, guidance, healing, courage or joy?

Read the book of Psalms.

The depth of emotion expressed by the writers makes this book relatable, encouraging, and comforting. It is a collection of poems, hymns, songs and prayers. They express deep and sincere faith in the midst of trials and tribulations.

The Hebrew word for "psalms" means "to pluck". This implies that the Psalms were to be accompanied by a stringed instrument. The poetic rhythm and figurative language used, clearly expresses the emotion the writer was feeling.

In the New Testament, believers are instructed to sing psalms:

> Ephesians 5:19 says, *"address one another in **psalms** and hymns and spiritual songs, singing and making melody to the Lord with your heart."*

> Colossians 3:16 says, *"Let the word of Christ dwell in you richly, teaching and admonishing one another in all wisdom, singing **psalms** and hymns and spiritual songs, with thankfulness in your hearts to God."*

Though this book was written many years ago, it is still relevant to believers today.

The Purpose: The book of Psalms was to be used as a hymnbook to sing praises to God. The word psalms is associated with playing instruments to accompany these songs.

The Author: The name of the author is at the start of each psalm. David is the most frequent writer. Other authors include: Solomon, Moses, the Sons of Korah, Asaph, Ethan and Ezahite. Some psalms have no designated author.

Time Period: This book was written between 1410-450 B.C.

Key Verse: Psalm 8:9

O Lord, our Lord, how majestic is your name in all the earth!

The Outline:

Originally, the book of Psalms was divided into 5 different books according to what was found within them.

- Book 1—Psalms 1-41
- Book 2—Psalms 42-72
- Book 3—Psalms 73-89
- Book 4—Psalms 90-106
- Book 5—Psalms 107-150

Types of Psalms:

- Psalms of Thanksgiving and Praise
- Psalms of Lament
- Psalms of Meditation, Prayer and Petition
- Psalms of Confidence and Trust
- Wisdom Psalms that Teach
- Historical Psalms
- Psalms of Suffering and Tears
- Imprecatory Psalms—Psalms that invoke judgment on their enemies.
- Kingship Psalms—Psalms that point to the future Messiah—the King of Kings or speak of David as a king.
- Acrostic Psalms—These psalms are written with special patterns using the Hebrew alphabet.

The book of Psalms is a hymnal, a prayer book, and a training guide. Every emotion a man can have is expressed from joy and sadness to anger, fear, doubt, repentance, praise, and trust. If you've felt it, Psalms expresses it. We could spend the rest of our lives reading the book of Psalms over and over and still not mine the depth of all that this book offers.

So let's get started!

Keep walking with the King!

Courtney

He is like a tree
planted by streams of water
that yields its fruit in season.
Psalm 1:3

Reflection Question:

This psalm depicts the characteristics of a godly person who loves God's Word and God's ways versus a wicked person.

What fruit are you seeing in your life as a result of your love for God and His Word? Is there anything in your life that causes you to not produce fruit?

Psalm 1

S—The S stands for *Scripture*

O—The O stands for *Observation*

A—The A stands for *Application*

K—The K stands for *Kneeling in Prayer*

Serve the Lord with fear, and rejoice with trembling.
Psalm 2:11

Reflection Question:

God calls the kings of the earth to surender to him and fear Him. We are to rejoice with trembling. A proper fear of God leads to rejoicing because we know how safe we are with him.

In what ways do you fear God and how does that affect your daily life?

Psalm 2

S—The S stands for *Scripture*

O—The O stands for *Observation*

A—The A stands for *Application*

K—The K stands for *Kneeling in Prayer*

But you, O Lord,
are a shield about me,
my glory,
and the lifter of my head.
Psalm 3:3

Reflection Question:

In a difficult situation, David chose to lift his eyes to the Lord and acknowledge His power. He has a deep trust in God.

As you go through trials, how can you choose to increase your faith instead of increasing your fears?

Psalm 3

S—The S stands for *Scripture*

O—The O stands for *Observation*

A—The A stands for *Application*

K—The K stands for *Kneeling in Prayer*

Be angry,
and do not sin.
Psalm 4:4

Reflection Question:

David instructed his people what to do when they found themselves getting angry: do not sin, search your heart, be still, offer right sacrifices and trust in the Lord.

How can you apply these instructions to your life when you feel anger creeping into your heart?

Psalm 4

S—The S stands for *Scripture*

O—The O stands for *Observation*

A—The A stands for *Application*

K—The K stands for *Kneeling in Prayer*

O Lord, in the morning
you hear my voice.
Psalm 5:3

Reflection Question:

David woke up with God on His mind. He made it a priority for God to hear his voice in the morning. This means he prayed out loud at the beginning of his day.

Does God hear your voice in the morning? If not, how can you rearrange your priorities to make time for prayer in the morning?

Psalm 5

S—The S stands for *Scripture*

O—The O stands for *Observation*

A—The A stands for *Application*

K—The K stands for *Kneeling in Prayer*

Every night I flood my bed with tears;
I drench my couch with my weeping.
The Lord has heard my plea.
Psalm 6:6-7

Reflection Question:

David was so discouraged that he could not sleep. His bed was flooded with tears but He knew that God saw him and heard His prayers.

Have you ever cried out to God feeling like God has abandoned you, only to later realize that He was strengthening you?

Psalm 6

S—The S stands for *Scripture*

O—The O stands for *Observation*

A—The A stands for *Application*

K—The K stands for *Kneeling in Prayer*

My shield is with God
who saves the upright in heart.
Psalm 7:10

Reflection Question:

David was crying out to the Lord for justice, deliverance and vindication, while asking God to search his heart.

Have you ever been blamed falsely for something? How did you handle it and how was God your shield?

Psalm 7

S—The S stands for *Scripture*

O—The O stands for *Observation*

A—The A stands for *Application*

K—The K stands for *Kneeling in Prayer*

O Lord, our Lord,
how majestic is your name
in all the earth!
Psalm 8:9

Reflection Question:

David beautifully expresses the glory and majesty of God in this psalm of praise.

How do you catch a glimpse of God's love for you through the moon, the stars and all of His creation?

Psalm 8

S—The S stands for *Scripture*

O—The O stands for *Observation*

A—The A stands for *Application*

K—The K stands for *Kneeling in Prayer*

Those who know your name
put their trust in you, for you,
O Lord, have not forsaken
those who seek you.
Psalm 9:10

Reflection Question:

Those who know God's name have a real relationship with him. We trust in Him and seek Him.

How does the assurance of knowing that God will never forsake you, comfort you when you struggle with unanswered prayer, fall into sin or face difficult trials?

Psalm 9

S—The S stands for *Scripture*

O—The O stands for *Observation*

A—The A stands for *Application*

K—The K stands for *Kneeling in Prayer*

The Lord is King
forever and ever.
Psalm 10:16

Reflection Question:

The enemy is always trying to destroy and tear down. After David writes of his affliction from his enemies, he affirms his confidence in God as King forever.

In the midst of evil that is all around us, how does knowing that God has all things in His control, comfort you?

Psalm 10

S—The S stands for *Scripture*

O—The O stands for *Observation*

A—The A stands for *Application*

K—The K stands for *Kneeling in Prayer*

For the Lord is righteous;
He loves righteous deeds;
the upright shall behold his face.
Psalm 11:7

Reflection Question:

God makes his presence known to the righteous and allows them to behold his face in the midst of turmoil.

How have you seen the face of God in your darkest times?

Psalm 11

S—The S stands for *Scripture*

O—The O stands for *Observation*

A—The A stands for *Application*

K—The K stands for *Kneeling in Prayer*

The words of the Lord
are pure words,
like silver refined in a furnace.
Psalm 12:6

Reflection Question:

David lived in a generation full of deceivers and prideful people. He contrasted their words with Gods. God's word is pure.

As a believer, how can you be accountable to speak truth with every word that you say?

Psalm 12

S—The S stands for *Scripture*

O—The O stands for *Observation*

A—The A stands for *Application*

K—The K stands for *Kneeling in Prayer*

I will sing to the Lord,
because he has dealt
bountifully with me.
Psalm 13:6

Reflection Question:

David opens his heart and shares his raw emotions, but still chooses to praise God in the depths of difficulties.

Are you in the midst of a trial? Despite your difficulties, what can you praise God for today?

Psalm 13

S—The S stands for *Scripture*

O—The O stands for *Observation*

A—The A stands for *Application*

K—The K stands for *Kneeling in Prayer*

The fool says in his heart, "There is no God." Psalm 14:1

Reflection Question:

David reflects on those who reject God and calls them fools. It's interesting to note where they deny God – it's in their hearts. Verse 2 says the Lord is looking down from heaven to see if there are any who seek him.

We may have a lot of intellectual knowledge about God but ultimately our decisions are made by the loves and passions of our heart. How is your heart today? Is it seeking God or seeking pleasure and how can you realign your heart with the heart of God?

Psalm 14

_____

S—The S stands for *Scripture*

O—The O stands for *Observation*

A—The A stands for *Application*

K—The K stands for *Kneeling in Prayer*

He who walks blamelessly
and does what is right...
shall never be moved.
Psalm 15:1, 5

_____

Reflection Question:

David lists eleven ways we should live if we want to have sweet fellowship with God.

Which of these stood out to you as something you need to work on in your life?

Psalm 15

S—The S stands for *Scripture*

O—The O stands for *Observation*

A—The A stands for *Application*

K—The K stands for *Kneeling in Prayer*

In your presence
there is fullness of joy;
at your right hand are
pleasures forevermore.
Psalm 16:11

Reflection Question:

God will not abandon us! The pleasures of the world are empty but God's joy is full. God's presence is with us and he gives pleasure for both now and eternity.

Just because we are believers that does not mean we get to experience a trouble free life. But sometimes we focus too much on what our faith is costing us and we forget all the benefits! List below some of the benefits and pleasures of being a child of God.

Psalm 16

S—The S stands for *Scripture*

O—The O stands for *Observation*

A—The A stands for *Application*

K—The K stands for *Kneeling in Prayer*

Keep me as the
apple of your eye;
hide me in the
shadow of your wings.
Psalm 17:8

Reflection Question:

The "apple of your eye" and the "shadow of your wings" are two pictures that powerfully describe God's care for his people in danger. The pupil of the eye is the most sensitive part of the eye and the most protected. A mama bird protects her helpless little ones, with her wings.

In the midst of David's fears, he prayed. Is there something you are fearful about today? Pray and talk to God about your fears. Looking back, how has God faithfully protected you in times of trouble?

Psalm 17

S—The S stands for *Scripture*

O—The O stands for *Observation*

A—The A stands for *Application*

K—The K stands for *Kneeling in Prayer*

The Lord is my rock and
my fortress and my deliverer...
in whom I take refuge, my shield,
and the horn of my salvation, my
stronghold.
Psalm 18:2

Reflection Question:

David wrote this psalm of praise, celebrating the victory that God gave him over all his enemies.

What is an example of a victory that God gave you and how was He your rock during that time?

Psalm 18

S—The S stands for *Scripture*

O—The O stands for *Observation*

A—The A stands for *Application*

K—The K stands for *Kneeling in Prayer*

Let the words of my mouth
and the meditation of my heart
be acceptable in your sight,
O Lord, my rock and my redeemer.
Psalm 19:14

Reflection Question:

As David reflects on the glory of God seen in creation and the purity of God seen in His word, he then reflects on himself. David closes this Psalm by reflecting on his words and his heart. His one desire is to be acceptable in God's sight.

Take a moment and reflect on your own words this week. Then reflect on your heart's desires. Is there anything you need to confess or surrender to God? Write out a humble prayer of confession below.

Psalm 19

S—The S stands for *Scripture*

O—The O stands for *Observation*

A—The A stands for *Application*

K—The K stands for *Kneeling in Prayer*

Some trust in chariots
and some in horses,
but we trust in the name
of the Lord our God.
Psalm 20:7

Reflection Question:

David knew that others were trusting in their horses and chariots for success. David contrasts their trust in things, with his trust in God.

Sometimes we can be tempted to trust in something other than God to give us success – like our intellegence, money or even another person. What are you tempted to trust in other than God.

Psalm 20

S—The S stands for *Scripture*

O—The O stands for *Observation*

A—The A stands for *Application*

K—The K stands for *Kneeling in Prayer*

Be exalted, O Lord, in your strength!
We will sing and praise your power.
Psalm 21:13

_____

Reflection Question:

David and his people were celebrating and singing praises to God for the victory and blessings He had given them.

Have you celebrated the blessings God has given you in your life including answered prayers? Try writing a prayer or poem of praise below and be specific about something God has done for you or a loved one.

Psalm 21

S—The S stands for *Scripture*

O—The O stands for *Observation*

A—The A stands for *Application*

K—The K stands for *Kneeling in Prayer*

Those who seek him
shall praise the Lord!
Psalm 22:26

Reflection Question:

In this psalm, David referenced the crucifixion of Jesus. Then a promise is given – all of those all over the earth ,who seek the Lord, will not only find him but will praise Him!

God does not hide himself from his people. You have sought the Lord and found Him! There is no greater gift! How does remembering that God has revealed himself to you, lead you to praise him for your salvation? Who can you pray for today that does not know Christ? Write your prayer below.

Psalm 22

S—The S stands for *Scripture*

O—The O stands for *Observation*

A—The A stands for *Application*

K—The K stands for *Kneeling in Prayer*

He makes me lie down in green pastures.
He leads me beside still waters.
Psalm 23:2

Reflection Question:

This beautiful psalm depicts how God cares for us. Sheep do not always know what is best and so we need our Shepherd. When we are following him, we are safe and secure, even through the dark valleys of life.

Are you allowing your shepherd to lead you? In what areas of your life, do you need to step back and let God lead?

Psalm 23

S—The S stands for **Scripture**

O—The O stands for **Observation**

A—The A stands for **Application**

K—The K stands for **Kneeling in Prayer**

The earth is the Lord's
and the fullness thereof,
the world and those who dwell therein.
Psalm 24:1

Reflection Question:

Earlier in Psalms, David emphasized the glory of God seen in the heavens. In this Psalm, he focuses on the Earth and how everything on it belongs to God.

When you consider the earth and all that God has created here, what do you learn about your God?

Psalm 24

S—The S stands for *Scripture*

O—The O stands for *Observation*

A—The A stands for *Application*

K—The K stands for *Kneeling in Prayer*

Lead me in your truth and teach me... for you I wait all the day long.
Psalm 25:5

Reflection Question:

David lifted his heart to God during difficult times. He desired to be taught by the Lord, during his season of waiting.

A mature believer desires to be taught by the Lord. How are you being taught by the Lord and what have you learned by waiting on God to guide you?

Psalm 25

S—The S stands for *Scripture*

O—The O stands for *Observation*

A—The A stands for *Application*

K—The K stands for *Kneeling in Prayer*

For your steadfast love
is before my eyes,
and I walk in your faithfulness.
Psalm 26:3

Reflection Question:

The word "walk" is repeated multiple times in this Psalm. David resisted evil by walking with the Lord.

What does it mean to walk in faithfulness and how are you displaying this in your life?

Psalm 26

S—The S stands for *Scripture*

O—The O stands for *Observation*

A—The A stands for *Application*

K—The K stands for *Kneeling in Prayer*

I believe that I shall look
upon the goodness of the LORD
in the land of the living!
Psalm 27:13

Reflection Question:

David was in a dangerous situation because of evildoers who wanted to take his life. But David believed. He believed that he would see the goodness of God, in the midst of his struggles and so he had courage to wait on the Lord.

How does your belief that God is good comfort you in the midst of your fears or trials?

Psalm 27

S—The S stands for *Scripture*

O—The O stands for *Observation*

A—The A stands for *Application*

K—The K stands for *Kneeling in Prayer*

The Lord is my strength
and my shield;
in him my heart trusts,
and I am helped.
Psalm 28:7

Reflection Question:

David learned to trust God in difficult situations, even when the Lord wasn't answering his prayers.

Think of a time when you felt like God was being silent. How did God eventually help you? How can that encourage you today as you wait on God to answer your prayers?

Psalm 28

S—The S stands for **Scripture**

O—The O stands for **Observation**

A—The A stands for **Application**

K—The K stands for **Kneeling in Prayer**

The voice of the Lord is powerful;
the voice of the Lord is full of majesty.
Psalm 29:4

Reflection Question:

In this Psalm, David speaks of hearing the powerful voice of God, through nature, over and over. It caused David to worship God.

We live in a noisy world. Technology runs 24/7. How do you hear God's voice and see his power on display in nature and how does that speak to your heart?

Psalm 29

S—The S stands for *Scripture*

O—The O stands for *Observation*

A—The A stands for *Application*

K—The K stands for *Kneeling in Prayer*

Weeping may tarry for the night,
but joy comes with the morning.
Psalm 30:5

Reflection Question:

David was expressing thanksgiving to God for rescuing him. After a season of darkness and weeping, joy had come!

The mercies of God are new every morning. Every sunrise brings the hope of a new and better day. How does a new morning, with a fresh start, wipe away your tears and give you hope?

Psalm 30

S—The S stands for *Scripture*

O—The O stands for *Observation*

A—The A stands for *Application*

K—The K stands for *Kneeling in Prayer*

In you, O Lord, do I take refuge;
let me never be put to shame.
Psalm 31:1

Reflection Question:

There is nothing that David trusts in, except God. He was not ashamed of his faith but rather praised God day in and day out, no matter how hard his trials had become.

Do you struggle to let your faith in God be known? Do you worry that God might not come through and somehow that will bring shame to yourself or God? In what area of your life do you need to be more bold with your faith?

Psalm 31

S—The S stands for *Scripture*

O—The O stands for *Observation*

A—The A stands for *Application*

K—The K stands for *Kneeling in Prayer*

I acknowledged my sin to you,
and I did not cover my iniquity...
and you forgave the iniquity of my sin.
Psalm 32:5

Reflection Question:

David confessed his sins to the Lord and rejoiced greatly because he was forgiven.

Are there any sins that you need to confess to God right now and receive His forgiveness?

Psalm 32

S—The S stands for *Scripture*

O—The O stands for *Observation*

A—The A stands for *Application*

K—The K stands for *Kneeling in Prayer*

Blessed is the nation
whose God is the Lord.
Psalm 33:12

———

Reflection Question:

This psalm is filled with praise and worship to the Lord.

What role does worship play in your life and how can you have a continual heart of praise?

Psalm 33

S—The S stands for *Scripture*

O—The O stands for *Observation*

A—The A stands for *Application*

K—The K stands for *Kneeling in Prayer*

The Lord is near to the brokenhearted and saves the crushed in spirit.
Psalm 34:18

Reflection Question:

David knew what it felt like to be broken. His spirit had been crushed through his trials. But God was near and heard his cries for help and delivered him from his afflictions.

Are you hurting today? Has something crushed you? The Lord is near and he wants to help you. Tell God your hurts. Ask him for help and deliverance. Let the Lord be your refuge, while you wait for healing.

Psalm 34

S—The S stands for *Scripture*

O—The O stands for *Observation*

A—The A stands for *Application*

K—The K stands for *Kneeling in Prayer*

Great is the Lord!
Psalm 35:27

Reflection Question:

In the midst of David's trials and turmoil, he continues to call on God for help and then praise the Lord for his greatness.

How do you respond to trials and turmoil in your life? Do you call out to God for help? Do you praise God for his greatness?

Psalm 35

S—The S stands for *Scripture*

O—The O stands for *Observation*

A—The A stands for *Application*

K—The K stands for *Kneeling in Prayer*

For with you is the fountain of life;
in your light do we see light.
Psalm 36:9

Reflection Question:

David spoke about the evil in this world and prayed that he would not be driven away by wickedness.

Is there anything in your heart that is pulling you away from God? Ask Him to shine His light upon it.

Psalm 36

S—The S stands for *Scripture*

O—The O stands for *Observation*

A—The A stands for *Application*

K—The K stands for *Kneeling in Prayer*

Delight yourself in the LORD,
and he will give you
the desires of your heart.
Psalm 37:4

Reflection Question:

When we are delighting in worldly things, our flesh longs for things that are not pleasing to the Lord. When we are delighting in God, He takes our old desires and makes them new.

Is there something you are longing for today, that perhaps is not from the Lord? Pray and ask God to exchange your desires for his desires and your will for his in your heart that is pulling you away from God? Ask Him to shine His light upon it.

Psalm 37

S—The S stands for **Scripture**

O—The O stands for **Observation**

A—The A stands for **Application**

K—The K stands for **Kneeling in Prayer**

I confess my iniquity;
I am sorry for my sin.
Psalm 38:18

Reflection Question:

David asked God for forgiveness of his sins. True repentance is sorrow over the sin itself not just the miserable results that sin can bring.

Is there a sin in your life that you need to confess? Confess it now. Consider if you have sinned against someone else and go to them and apologize today.

Psalm 38

S—The S stands for *Scripture*

O—The O stands for *Observation*

A—The A stands for *Application*

K—The K stands for *Kneeling in Prayer*

I will guard my ways,
that I may not sin with my tongue;
I will guard my mouth with a muzzle...
Psalm 39:1

Reflection Question:

In Psalm 39, David is emotional. He goes from from anger to crying. David worked hard to not sin with his mouth. Though he kept quiet, his feelings did not dissipate.

When you feel emotional, do you guard your mouth and keep it from sin? What can we learn from the heart of David, in today's Psalm?

Psalm 39

S—The S stands for *Scripture*

O—The O stands for *Observation*

A—The A stands for *Application*

K—The K stands for *Kneeling in Prayer*

He drew me up
from the pit of destruction...
and set my feet upon a rock
Psalm 40:2

Reflection Question:

David praised God for meeting his needs during difficult trials.

How have you seen God work in your life, by drawing you up from a pit of despair?

Psalm 40

S—The S stands for *Scripture*

O—The O stands for *Observation*

A—The A stands for *Application*

K—The K stands for *Kneeling in Prayer*

Even my close friend
in whom I trusted,
who ate my bread,
has lifted his heel against me.
Psalm 41:9

Reflection Question:

As David was sick in bed, he also endured a betrayal from a close friend. This verse was also spoken by Jesus in John 13:18, regarding Judas Iscariot's betrayal. But David remained steadfast in His confidence that God would never betray him.

Have you ever been betrayed by a close friend that you really trusted? How does knowing that both Jesus and David experienced betrayal comfort you? And how does knowing that God will never betray you, encourage you?

Psalm 41

S—The S stands for *Scripture*

O—The O stands for *Observation*

A—The A stands for *Application*

K—The K stands for *Kneeling in Prayer*

Why are you cast down, O my soul,
and why are you in turmoil within me?
Hope in God;
for I shall again praise him.
Psalm 42:5

Reflection Question:

The author, in these next two psalms, questions God many times as he also puts his hope and trust in Him.

Have you ever cried out to God so much that you've questioned where He is? How has God revealed Himself to you through those times?

Psalm 42

S—The S stands for **Scripture**

O—The O stands for **Observation**

A—The A stands for **Application**

K—The K stands for **Kneeling in Prayer**

Send out your light and your truth;
let them lead me.
Psalm 43:3

Reflection Question:

God's light and truth are faithful guides to the believer.

How is God's truth leading you today?

Psalm 43

S—The S stands for *Scripture*

O—The O stands for *Observation*

A—The A stands for *Application*

K—The K stands for *Kneeling in Prayer*

You are my King.
Psalm 44:4

Reflection Question:

The Jewish people were defeated by their enemy and felt humiliated and deserted by God.

Have you ever felt that God has hidden His face from you and how do you continue to seek Him through those feelings?

Psalm 44

S—The S stands for *Scripture*

O—The O stands for *Observation*

A—The A stands for *Application*

K—The K stands for *Kneeling in Prayer*

Your throne, O God,
is forever and ever.
Psalm 45:6

Reflection Question:

This psalm is a love song written for the wedding of a king. However, the underlying message is about Jesus Christ and His bride, the church.

Christ is our divine King. There is no successor. His kingdom is forever. How does knowing that the king of Kings and Lord of Lords loves you forever -- comfort and encourage you?

Psalm 45

S—The S stands for *Scripture*

O—The O stands for *Observation*

A—The A stands for *Application*

K—The K stands for *Kneeling in Prayer*

God is in the midst of her;
she shall not be moved;
God will help her when morning dawns.
Psalm 46:5

Reflection Question:

When we wake, God's help is not slow. He is with us in the mornings, throughout the day and all night.

God is our very present help in times of trouble. How have you experienced God's presence and help, in times of trouble?

Psalm 46

S—The S stands for *Scripture*

O—The O stands for *Observation*

A—The A stands for *Application*

K—The K stands for *Kneeling in Prayer*

Clap your hands, all peoples!
Shout to God with loud songs of joy!
Psalm 47:1

Reflection Question:

The people in this psalm were told to praise and exalt God.

Let's do it! Write your own psalm or poem or words of praise to God below.

Psalm 47

S—The S stands for *Scripture*

O—The O stands for *Observation*

A—The A stands for *Application*

K—The K stands for *Kneeling in Prayer*

Great is the LORD
and greatly to be praised
in the city of our God!
Psalm 48:1

Reflection Question:

God shows His people that He is their fortress and that He will guide them forever.

How does God's steadfast love encourage and help you when all of these horrible things are happening in the world.

Psalm 48

S—The S stands for *Scripture*

O—The O stands for *Observation*

A—The A stands for *Application*

K—The K stands for *Kneeling in Prayer*

Even the wise die;
the fool and the stupid alike must
perish
and leave their wealth to others.
Psalm 49:10

Reflection Question:

The psalmist reminds us that being wealthy does not prevent death and does not determine our salvation. The rich cannot take their money with them when they die. While the rich spend their lives building their homes and collecting money here on earth, the righteous trust in God.

In what ways are you tempted to trust more in your wealth than in God?

Psalm 49

S—The S stands for **Scripture**

O—The O stands for **Observation**

A—The A stands for **Application**

K—The K stands for **Kneeling in Prayer**

The one who
offers thanksgiving
as his sacrifice
glorifies me.
Psalm 50:23

Reflection Question:

This is our final Psalm in this study. It is fitting to remember this. This psalm talks about worshiping God with honesty and gratitude; not as a ritual or a disguise. May we continue to praise his name forever with glad and sincere hearts!

As you continue to live your life praising the Lord, how can you make sure you are worshiping the Lord with sincerity and not let it turn into a routine?

Psalm 50

S—The S stands for *Scripture*

O—The O stands for *Observation*

A—The A stands for *Application*

K—The K stands for *Kneeling in Prayer*

89490913R00061

Made in the USA
Lexington, KY
29 May 2018